USBORNE KEY SKI

C000174595

Wipe-clean
Finding out about
Plants

Illustrated by Marta Cabrol

Written by Jessica Greenwell
and Hannah Watson

Designed by Maddison Warnes

How much water
should we give
this plant?

Crock

Lem

Beaky

Expert advice from Dr. John Rostron
and Dr. Margaret Rostron

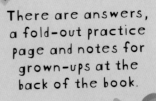

There are answers,
a fold-out practice
page and notes for
grown-ups at the
back of the book.

Series Editor: Felicity Brooks

2

Plants, bulbs and seeds

Tig has come to see Ant's garden. Copy the words from the yellow panel onto the labels to help Ant name all the plants and trees.

Fruit tree   Grass

Flowers   Shrub

Tig

This little tree is called a shrub.

Ant

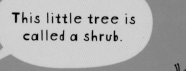

s h r u b

Tig wants to grow a garden of his own. Draw some more plants on his garden plan.

I'd like lots of pretty flowers in my garden.

Definitely one of these

Maybe a tree here

Lots of these

Most plants grow from either a seed or a bulb.
Seeds and bulbs need water and warmth to start to grow.
It takes time for them to grow into plants and flowers.

Squawk!

Lem is going to buy some things Tig will need to grow plants in the soil in his garden. Circle four things that Tig might need.

Hmmm... I don't think Tig will need pet food.

Lem

umbrellas

watering can

fishing nets

bulbs

trowels

sponges

seeds

mop

pet food

Ant is writing some instructions for Tig on how to plant his seeds and bulbs. Finish the words below to complete the sentences.

1. Plant some s _ _ _ _ and b _ _ _ _ in some soil.

2. Give them plenty of w _ _ _ _ and time to g _ _ _ .

3. Wait a few weeks for them to start to grow into p _ _ _ _ _ _ .

Starting to grow

Bulbs and seeds have a store of food inside them that they use as they begin to grow.

Squawk!

Tig planted a bulb and a seed in some soil and watered them.
The pictures below show what happened to them over a few weeks.
Write 1, 2, 3 or 4 in the boxes to put the pictures in the right order.

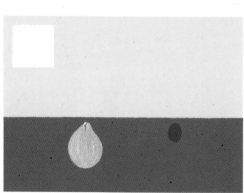

Wow, the bulb and the seed are growing into plants!

Let's make a scrapbook about your plants growing.

We could label the pictures, too.

Ant and Tig have drawn pictures of the plants that grew. Draw lines from each of Ant's labels to the correct part of the plant. Next, copy the words to label Tig's picture for him.

flower

leaf

stem

roots

There are some diagrams on the fold-out page at the back of the book, if you need help.

I've written a label for the bulb. Draw a line to the correct part of the plant.

Finish these labels

bulb

What do plants need?

Squawk!

Plants need air, water, energy from sunlight to make food, and the right temperature (amount of heat) to stay alive.

Tig's friends are talking about what they think the plants in his garden need to stay healthy. Put a tick next to three ideas that you think are right.

Plants need water to stay alive.

Lep

Maybe the plants need to eat vegetables to stay healthy.

Cheeky

I think plants need sunlight.

Baz

Plants need to be kept at the right temperature.

No, all plants really need is music.

Tan-tan

Ant is making Tig a guide on how to keep his plants healthy. Put a line through the incorrect words so that each sentence makes sense. Trace over the pictures to complete Ant's guide.

Here's everything you need to know, to keep your plants healthy.

Looking after plants

Plants need to take in

water   juice

through their roots to stay healthy.

Plants need

sunlight   music

to make their own food.

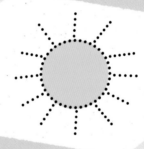

Plants need the right

temperature   breakfast

to grow well.

How much water?

Tig has gone on holiday and his friends are looking after his plants for him. They've forgotten how much water he said they needed...

I'm going to have a guess and try 1 teaspoon each week.

I'll give this plant a can of water every few days.

I think Tig said 3 big buckets every day, so I'll try that.

Put a dot next to the animal you think might be right.

After two weeks, their plants looked like this:

Lem

Tan-tan

Crock

Circle the plant you think looks the healthiest.

Lem's plant   Tan-tan's plant   Crock's plant

Squawk!

Different kinds of plants need different amounts of water.
A plant could die if it has too much or too little water.

Compare how each plant looked after two weeks.
Choose three words from the yellow panel to describe
each plant and copy them into the chart below.

I think my plant looked quite yellow!

yellow   alive   soggy   rotten   dry

crisp   healthy   green   soaked

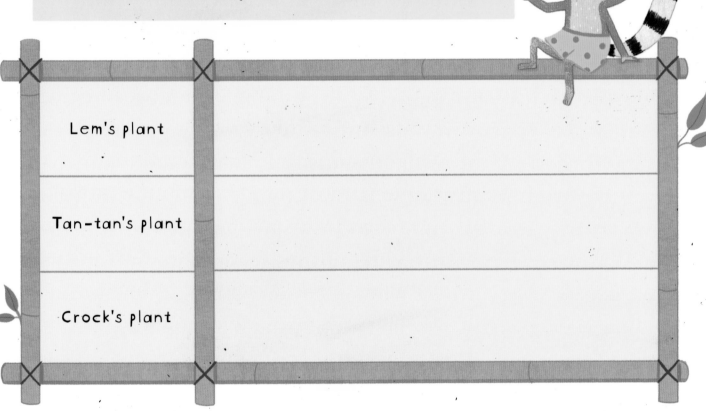

Lem's plant

Tan-tan's plant

Crock's plant

Who do you think gave their plant the right amount
of water? Write the name of the animal here:

....

What temperature?

Squawk!

Different kinds of plants need different temperatures to grow well.
If a plant is at the wrong temperature, it will struggle to grow.

These animals are looking after Tig's greenhouse plants, but he forgot
to tell them what temperature the greenhouse needs to be.

They decide to test whether the plants grow better
with the temperature set to 'warm' or to 'hot'.

Circle something in the picture that tells the animals the temperature of
the greenhouse. Circle something they could use to measure the plant.

Help Baz complete the chart showing the results of the animals' tests. Trace the numbers then fill in the final column.

Find the difference between the plant heights to work out how much the plant grew.

	Plant height at the start	Plant height after 2 weeks	How much did it grow?
Warm greenhouse	6cm	9cm	
Hot greenhouse	9cm	10cm	

Don't forget, 'cm' stands for 'centimetres'.

Did the plant grow more when it was warm or when it was hot in the greenhouse? Circle the answer below.

warm

hot

Wipe the pictures clean.

Should the animals set the greenhouse temperature to 'warm' or to 'hot' for the rest of Tig's holiday? Circle the correct answer above.

How much light?

Squawk!

Don't forget, plants need sunlight to grow. They use energy from sunlight to make their own food.

Lep and Crock decide to buy some more plants for Tig as a present. They can't agree on the best place to put them.

We should put the plants in a sunny spot.

Lep ✔

Crock

I think the plants will grow best in the dark.

Who do you think is correct?
Write the animal's name here: ....

How could you explain to the animals the reason for your answer? Put a tick next to the two facts you could use.

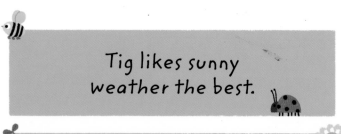

Tig likes sunny weather the best.

Plants use energy from sunlight to make food.

Plants need sunlight to grow.

The plants will look prettier in the sunshine.

Lep notices that the plants are growing towards the sunlight, and wonders why. Tick one idea that you think is correct.

Lep wonders what would happen if she covered the plants up, so the sunlight couldn't reach them. Draw a star (★) next to the picture that you think shows what would happen.

The plant would go to sleep.

The plant would have to make food another way.

The plant wouldn't grow well as it wouldn't be able to make food.

Plants and the seasons

Tig has been to the same place on holiday in spring, summer, autumn and winter. He noticed that the tree outside his window looked different in each season, and he described it in his diary.

Finish the words to complete my sentences, using the pictures to help you.

Spring

The tree is covered in little _ _ _ _ _ _ _ called blossom.

Summer

Now the tree has green leaves and small red _ _ _ _ _ _ .

Autumn

Orange and brown _ _ _ _ _ _ _ fall from the tree.

Winter

There are no leaves left, but the tree looks lovely in the _ _ _ _ _

Plants and some trees change throughout the year. They can look very different in each of the four seasons. For example, many flowers bloom in the summer when it's warm and then they die in the cold winter.

Tig took a photograph of this flowering plant in each season. Draw lines to match each picture to the correct season. The first one has been done for you.

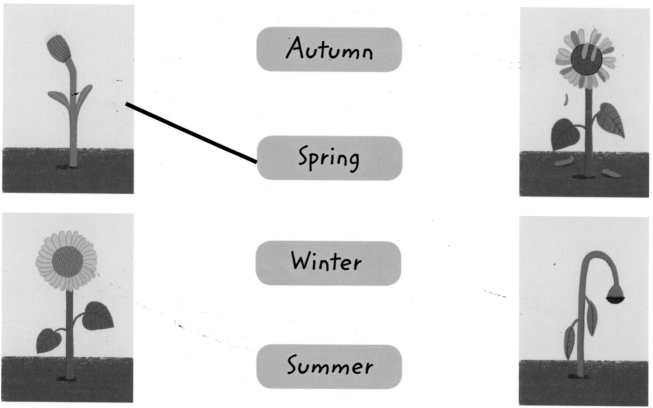

Autumn

Spring

Winter

Summer

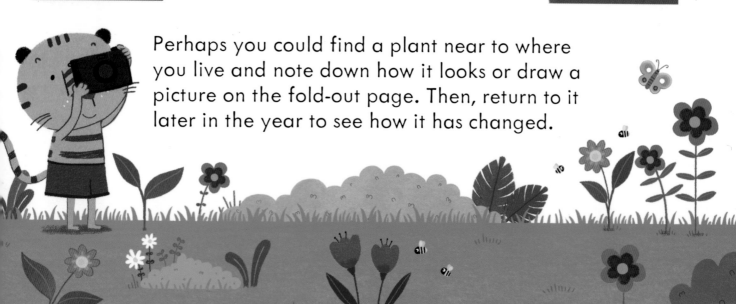

Perhaps you could find a plant near to where you live and note down how it looks or draw a picture on the fold-out page. Then, return to it later in the year to see how it has changed.

Plant habitats

Squawk!

A habitat is the place where a plant grows naturally.
For example, the natural habitat of a cactus is a desert.

Ant has visited three different habitats and painted pictures
of himself in each one. Help him label his pictures by writing
the habitat name under each picture.

desert

woodland

sea

....

....

....

A microhabitat is a small area that is specially suited to the
plant that grows there, e.g. a rock with moss growing on it.

Find a microhabitat (a rock with moss growing on it) in
one of the pictures above and circle it with your pen.

Next, help Ant label the plants he saw in each habitat. Choose the correct plant name from the blue strip to copy under each picture.

seaweed   fern   cactus

....

Choose a word from the yellow strip to help Ant complete each of these sentences about the plants in their habitats.

hot   shady   underwater

Ferns are often found in __ __ __ __ __ woodland spots.

A cactus grows well in the __ __ __ , dry desert.

Seaweed is found __ __ __ __ __ __ __ __ __ __ __ .

Making new plants

When a plant makes a new plant, it's called reproduction. Bees and other insects help plants reproduce by moving pollen (a powder made inside flowers) from one plant to another. This is called pollination.

Squawk!

Help Froggy choose one animal below that helps plants to make new plants. Circle it with your pen.

Baz is drawing a picture of a plant he spotted today. Trace the dots to help him finish it. Put a star next to the part of the plant you think might attract insects.

This flower has big, colourful petals and a sweet smell.

There is a sweet liquid called nectar in the middle of flowers. Bees like to drink it. As a bee drinks nectar, pollen sticks to its body and then gets carried to another flower. That flower can then make seeds so that a new plant can grow.

Squawk!

Lep and Lem want to write a story about a bee and a flower. Lep has written the sentences and Lem has drawn the pictures. Draw lines to match each sentence to its picture.

1. A bee sees a beautiful flower and it smells sweet.

2. The bee sips nectar from the flower and pollen sticks to its fuzzy back.

3. The bee flies away to visit the next flower.

The animals think about other ways pollen travels from plant to plant. Circle one idea that is correct.

The wind could blow pollen from one plant to another.

Maybe pollen travels on a bicycle to the next plant.

Fruits and seeds

Plants make seeds so that new plants can grow from them.
You can often find seeds inside the fruits made by plants.

Squawk!

Ant has some fruit trees in his garden with fruit growing on them. Choose words from the yellow strip to help him label the trees. Then, draw a line from each word in the yellow strip to its matching fruit below.

_ _ _ _ _ _ _   _ _ _ _ _ _   _ _ _ _ _ _ _   _ _ _ _ _

tree   tree   tree   tree

orange   apple   cherry   avocado

Yum!

Ant had a picnic with friends and they ate some of the fruits in his garden but left these seeds...

orange pip

apple pip

avocado stone

cherry stone

'Stone' and 'pip' are also words for 'seed'.

Ant decided he'd like to see what each seed looked like inside its fruit, so he cut some fruits in half. Using the names of the seeds, label each fruit below.

An avocado stone is much bigger than a tiny apple pip, but they're both still seeds.

_ _ _ _ _ _ _

_ _ _ _ _ _ _

_ _ _ _ _ _ _

_ _ _ _ _ _ _

Finding out about plants quiz

Find out how much you can remember about plants by doing this quiz.
Answers are on page 24.

A. Tig needs to add labels to the things on his market stall. Help him
by drawing a line to match each label to the correct item.

| Flowers | Fruit tree | Shrub | Seeds | Bulbs |

B. The mice have written a list
of everything that they think
plants need to grow. Put a tick
next to the three things on
their list that are correct.

What plants need to grow

- sunlight
- music
- water
- friends
- frost
- right temperature

C. Lem decided to grow one plant in a dark cupboard and one on a sunny windowsill to see which would grow best. Draw a circle around the plant that you think was grown on the windowsill.

Plant 1

Plant 2

D. Draw lines to match each of these plants to the correct set of instructions. Think about the natural habitat of each plant to help you.

Forest fern

Desert cactus

Swamp blueberry

Instruction 1

Water every day to keep soil damp. Fruit will ripen in August.

Instruction 2

Place in a cool, shady spot and water twice per week.

Instruction 3

Place in a warm, sunny spot and water once per week.

E. Choose words from the blue strip to write into the gaps in this story.

pollen   nectar   flower

A bee spotted a colourful _____.

He drank its _____ and _____ stuck to his back.

Then he flew to the next flower.

F. Draw lines to match these seeds to the fruits they came from.

cherry stone   orange pip   avocado stone   apple pip

Quiz answers

A.

Shrub   Seeds   Flowers   Bulbs   Fruit tree

B. Sunlight, water, right temperature

C. Plant 1 was grown on the windowsill.

D. Forest fern – Instruction 2, Desert cactus – Instruction 3, Swamp blueberry – Instruction 1

E. A bee spotted a colourful <u>flower</u>.
He drank its <u>nectar</u> and <u>pollen</u> stuck to his back.

F.

Score 1 point for each correct answer and write your score in this box: If you want to get a higher score, wipe the pages clean and try again.

19